U P B E A T.

For Piano

Alison Bowditch

CONTENTS

Foreword by Maureen Cox

Pigs Might Fly 4
Dizzy Daze 5
Get Real! 6
Chinatown 7
Lucky Feeling 8
Shadows 9
Toy Soldiers 10
Melancholy Blues 11
Easy Trapezey 12
Jack Frost 13
Tranquility 14
No Worries 15

Level 1

First published 1997
by Subject Publications
   Beech House
   Broadstone
   Dorset BH18 9NJ
   Tel: 01202-696907
   Fax:01202-657743

ISBN 1 898771 04 9

★ ★ ★ ★ ★ ★

Acknowledgements

From the sale of this book the Composer and Publishers will make a donation to The Beethoven Fund For Deaf Children (Charity Registration no. 282844).

★ ★ ★ ★ ★ ★

Printed by Pardy & Son (Printers) Ltd.,
Parkside, Ringwood, Hampshire BH24 3SF
Tel: 01425 471433
Fax: 01425 478923

For Hannah

★ ★ ★ ★ ★ ★

ABOUT THE COMPOSER

Alison Bowditch obtained at Cardiff University the prestigious Bachelor of Music honours degree with musical composition as a principal specialisation. She studied piano under Richard McMahon and oboe under John Williams. She embarked upon a teaching career after completing the one-year post-graduate certificate course at Rolle College, Exmouth.

Alison teaches a wide range of woodwind instruments, as well as piano and voice, to pupils of all ages. She successfully combines her work as a composer with her rôle as a mother of three young children. In addition to composing for the Playing Is Fun series, Alison finds time to play in a county orchestra and to fulfil professional engagements as a musician in her own right.

★ ★ ★ ★ ★ ★

FOREWORD

The Playing Is Fun series aims to capture your imagination and increase your enjoyment of music. Whatever your age, you will find these original compositions for piano or keyboard both exciting and inspiring. Among the many and varied rhythmical styles are those of jazz, swing, rock, blues and boogie.

Each piece is a challenge and an adventure with its own mood and rhythm for you to discover. To help you with each interpretation, the composer has suggested a suitable tempo and style; she has also indicated possible fingering wherever appropriate. As you progress, you will meet a widening range of key signatures, time signatures and rhythm patterns.

At every level, Upbeat for Piano by Alison Bowditch is great fun to hear and play.

Maureen Cox

Pigs Might Fly

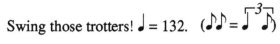

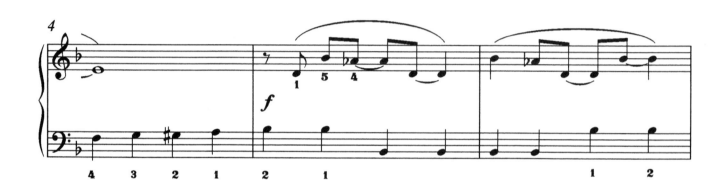

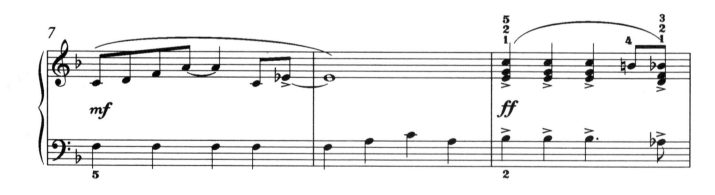

Dizzy Daze

Get Real!

Chinatown

Lucky Feeling

Bright and energetic. ♩ = 148.

Shadows

With mystery. ♩ = 142.

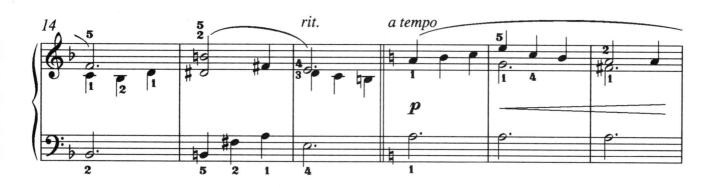

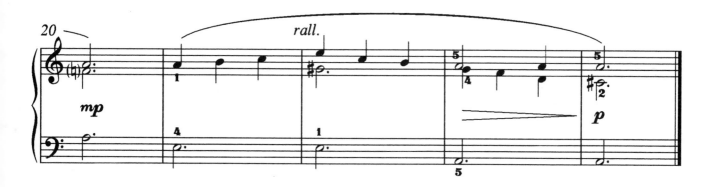

Toy Soldiers

In strict time. ♩ = 120.

Melancholy Blues

Easy Trapezey

Feel one-in-a-bar. ♩. = 56.

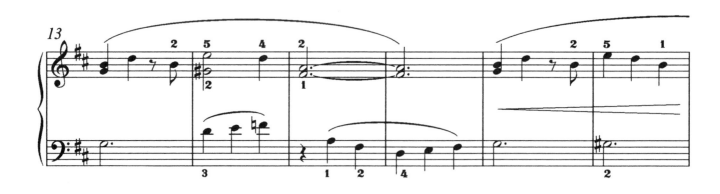

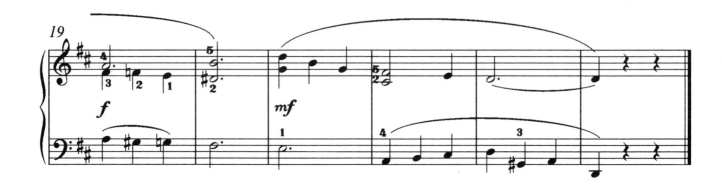

Jack Frost

With an icy chill. ♩ = 90.

Tranquility

Restful and smooth. ♩ = 78.

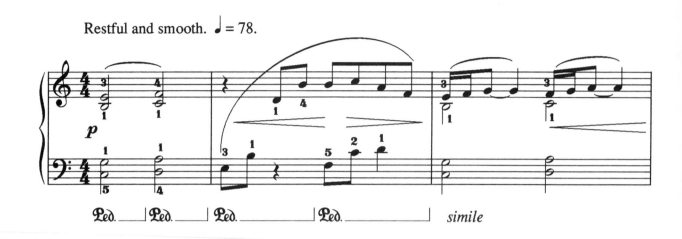

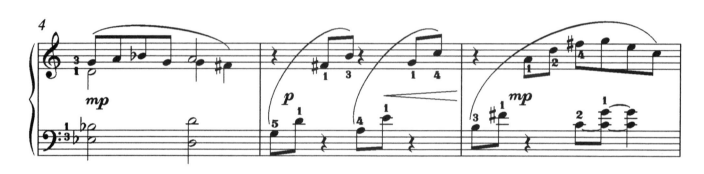

No Worries

Relaxed and easy. ♩ = 132.

(say 'yeah!')

THEORY IS FUN GRADE 1
Maureen Cox

Treble clef, bass clef, notes and letter names. Time names and values; dotted notes, tied notes and rests.
Accidentals. Tones and semitones.
Key signatures and scales (C, G, D & F Major).
Degrees of the scale, intervals and tonic triads.
Simple time signatures and bar-lines.
Writing music and answering rhythms.
Musical terms dictionary and list of signs.

ISBN 0-9516940-8-1

THEORY IS FUN GRADE 2
Maureen Cox

Major key signatures and scales to 3 sharps or 3 flats.
A, D and E minor key signatures and scales.
Degrees of the scale and intervals. Tonic triads and accidentals.
Piano keyboard, tones and semitones.
Simple time signatures. Grouping notes and rests. Triplets.
Two ledger lines below and above the staves.
Writing four-bar rhythms
More musical terms and signs.

ISBN 1-898771-02-2

THEORY IS FUN GRADE 3
Maureen Cox

Major and minor key signatures to 4 sharps or 4 flats.
Harmonic and melodic minor scales.
Degrees of the scale, intervals and tonic triads.
Simple and compound time signatures. Grouping notes and rests. Transposition at the octave.
More than two ledger lines.
Writing four-bar rhythms. Anacrusis. Phrases.
More musical terms and signs.

ISBN 1-898771-00-6

THEORY IS FUN GRADE 4
Maureen Cox

All key signatures to 5 sharps or 5 flats. Alto clef; chromatic scale, double sharps and flats. Technical names of notes in the diatonic scale. Simple and compound time: duple, triple, quadruple. Primary triads: tonic, subdominant and dominant.
All diatonic intervals up to an octave. Recognising ornaments.
Four-bar rhythms and rhythms to words.
Families of orchestral instruments and their clefs.
More musical terms, including French.

ISBN 1-898771-01-4

THEORY IS FUN GRADE 5
Maureen Cox

All key signatures to 7 sharps or 7 flats. Tenor clef and scales.
Compound intervals: major, minor, perfect, diminished and augmented. Irregular time signatures: quintuple and septuple.
Tonic, supertonic, subdominant and dominant chords.
Writing at concert pitch. Short and open score. Orchestral instruments in detail. Composing a melody for instrument or voice. Perfect, imperfect and plagal cadences.
More musical terms, including German.

ISBN 0-9516940-9-X

READING
CONTEMPORARY
ELECTRIC BASS

Performance Studies in Funk, Rock, Disco, Jazz, and Other Music Styles

Rich Appleman

Berklee Press

Director: Dave Kusek
Managing Editor: Debbie Cavalier
Marketing Manager: Ola Frank
Sr. Writer/Editor: Jonathan Feist

ISBN 0-634-01338-6

1140 Boylston Street
Boston, MA 02215-3693 USA
(617) 747-2146

Visit Berklee Press Online at
www.berkleepress.com

DISTRIBUTED BY

HAL•LEONARD®
CORPORATION
7777 W. BLUEMOUND RD. P.O. BOX 13819
MILWAUKEE, WISCONSIN 53213

Visit Hal Leonard Online at
www.halleonard.com

TABLE OF CONTENTS

Section I   **Pages**
Regular bass line rhythms.
"Walking Bass", "Two Feel"   4-25
Section II
Syncopated, more active bass lines
and rhythms. Eighth-note feel. Top 40,
Soft Rock, Country/Western, Radio
and TV Jingles   26-51
Section III
Busier, more syncopated lines
and rhythms. Eighth and sixteenth note
feel. Funk, Rock, Disco, Contemporary
Musical Theatre   52-74
Section IV
Vamps, Repetitive phrases using
moderately active rhythms   75-79
Section V
Reading exercises. Varied styles of bass
lines and rhythms found in professional
performing situations   80-111

FOREWORD

Contemporary Electric Bass Rhythms mean many things to many people; fast repetitive funk vamps, long low sustained notes behind a singer, walking lines composed on the spot that shape a framework for a jazz soloist, and many more.

The rhythms and bass lines in this book are representative of what I've been playing in many different areas of performance — Theatre, Pop, Recording, Jazz, Dance, Funk, Fusion, Latin, Disco . . .

The Contemporary bassist must play, read, and compose in a variety of different styles.

Some general rules to think about:

- Don't get fooled by the apparent simplicity of basic foundation lines and rhythms. It takes good musicianship to play them right!
- Develop a vocabulary of basic rhythms and styles and use it as a basis on which to constantly expand. Be as versatile and flexible as possible.
- Be solid and supportive; Develop a good time feel and good sound before trying to be an out front lead-type player.

Some hints for practicing these exercises:

- Always play slowly and perfectly when learning something new.
- Play at different tempos with different phrasing.
- Try playing the lines and rhythms in all keys. Memorize the lines you especially like and expand upon them.
- Chord symbols have been omitted to make certain that the book is used to develop *reading* skills.
- Don't just play notes . . . make music!

Good Luck,

Richard E. Appleman
Chairman, Bass Department
BERKLEE COLLEGE OF MUSIC

SECTION I

Regular Bass Line Rhythms. "Walking Bass", "Two Feel".

To Coda ⊕

opt.

D.C. al coda

Coda
⊕

fine

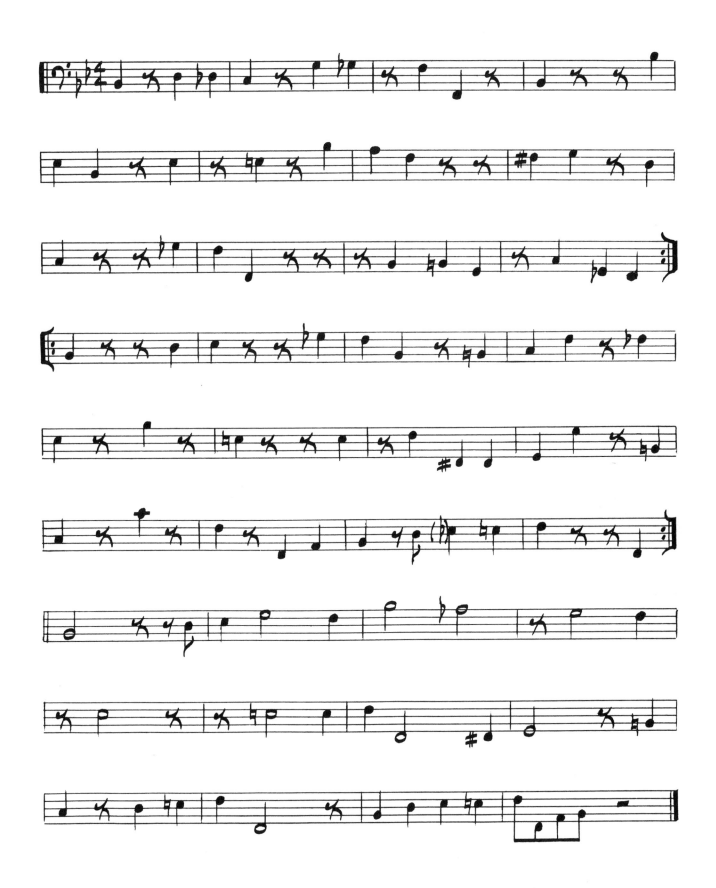

To Coda

1.

2.

D.C. al coda

Coda

fine

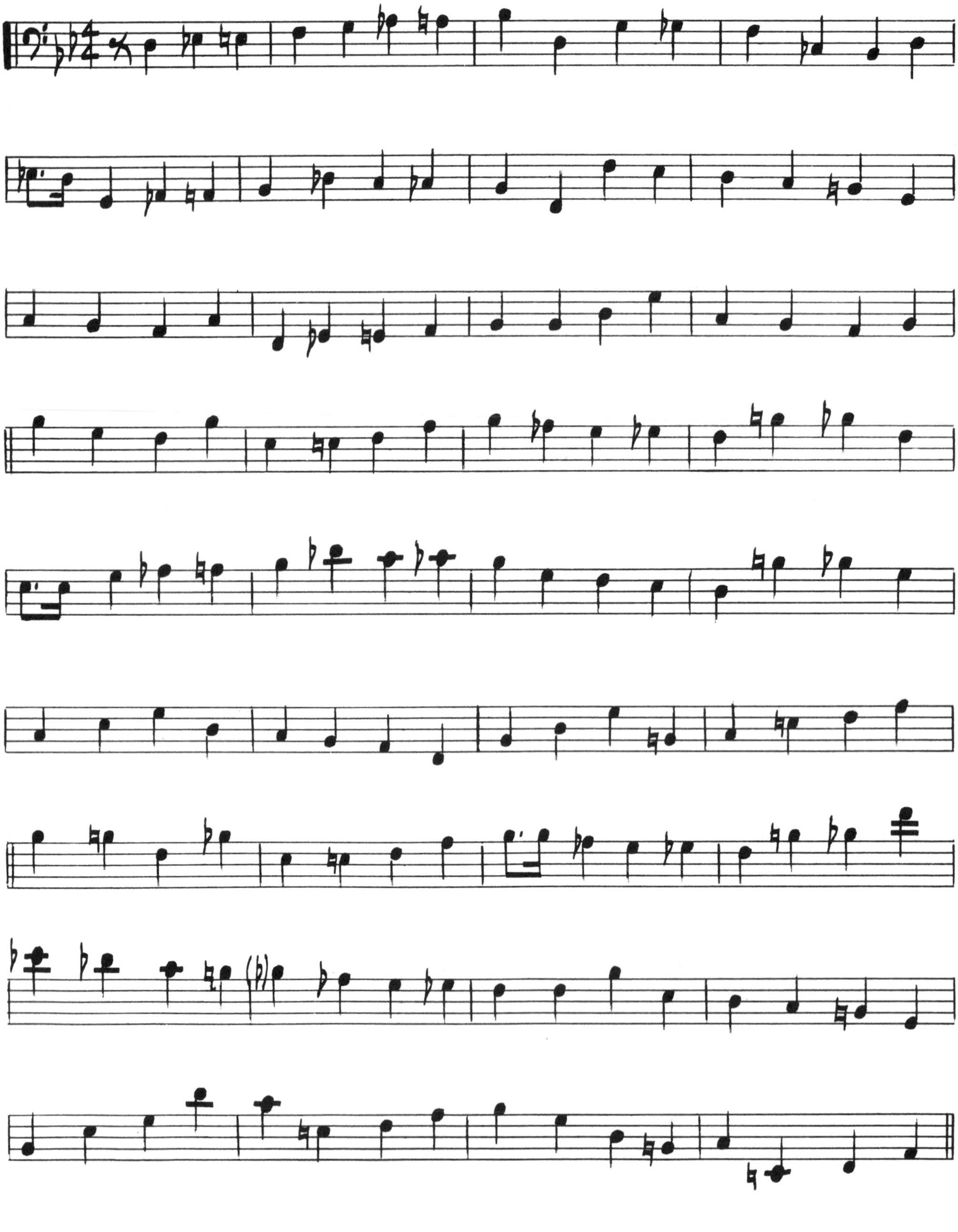

16

17

"2"

18

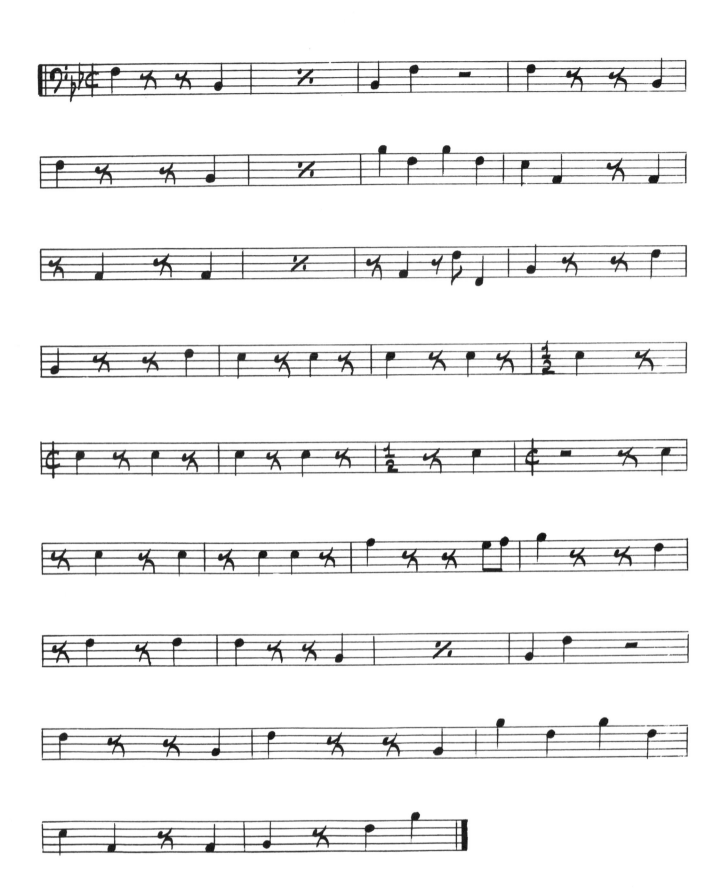

22

Med."2"feel

To Coda ⊕

1.

2.

Coda ⊕

March

SECTION II

Syncopated, More Active Bass Lines and Rhythms. Eighth-Note Feel.
Top 40, Soft Rock, Country/Western, Radio and TV Jingles.

To Coda

D.C. al coda

Coda

30

31

34

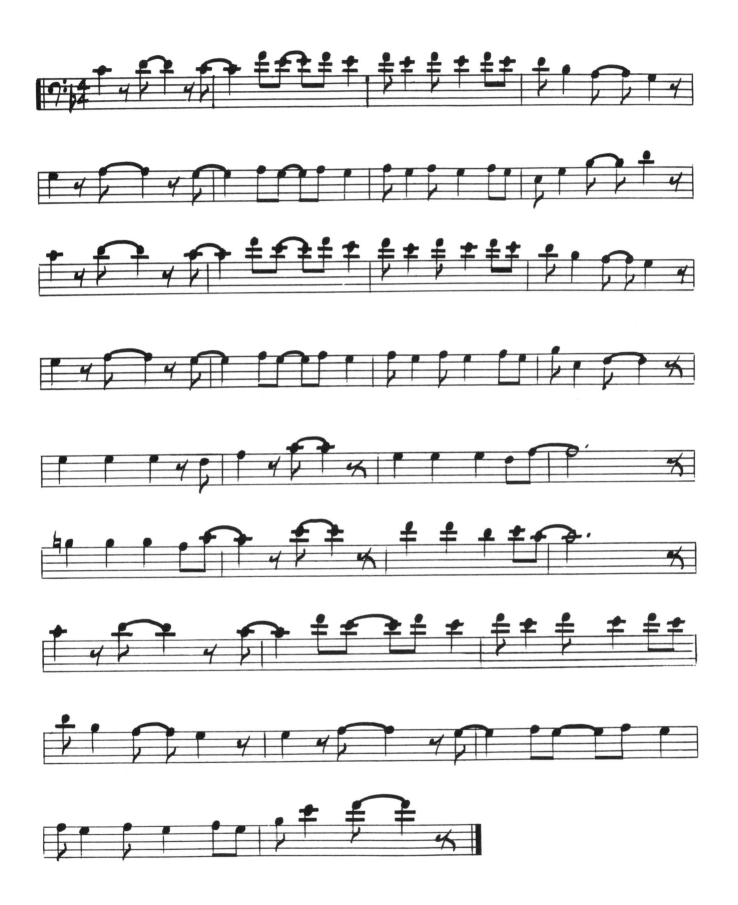

To Coda

D.C. al coda

Coda

D.S. al coda

Fine

46

48

* Note

51

SECTION III

Busier, More syncopated Lines and Rhythms. Eighth and Sixteenth
Note Feel. Funk, Rock, Disco, Contemporary Musical Theatre.

Vamp

♪ = ♩

Usually written

Written

Long Notes

56

64

To Coda ⊕

D.C. al coda

Coda ⊕

70

To Coda

D.C. al coda

Coda

To Coda

Coda

SECTION IV
Vamps, Repetitive Phrases Using Moderately Active Rhythms.

76

Dead Note = X

SECTION V

Reading Exercises. Varied Styles of Bass Lines and Rhythms
Found in Professional Performing Situations.

84

Ballad

93

94

To Coda

D.C. al coda

Coda

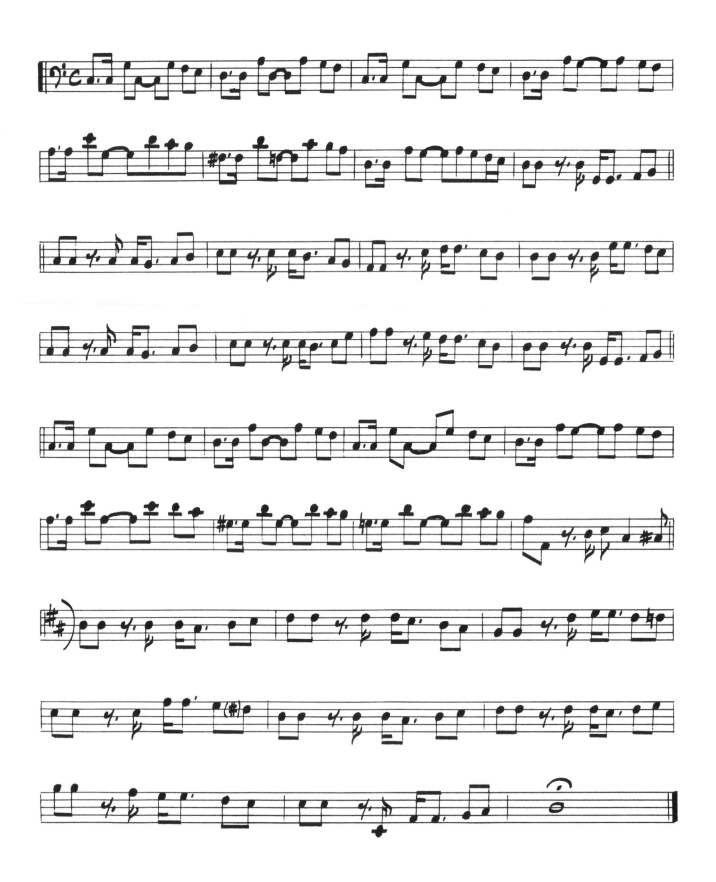

101

Latin

104

105

To Coda

D.C. al coda

Coda

D.C. al coda

Coda

109

110